Sunrise

W9-CPV-816

DATE DUE			
DEC 08			
NOV 2 2 1994			
JAN 1 2 1995			
GAYLORD			PRINTED IN U.S.A.

ABDUL
Abul-Bul Amir
&
IVAN
Skavinsky
Skavar

ABDUL
Abul-Bul Amir
&
IVAN
Skavinsky
Skavar

Illustrated by
DEBORAH RAY

MACRAE SMITH COMPANY
Philadelphia

*"The horror of that moment," the King went on,
"I shall never, never forget!"
"You will, though," the Queen said, "if you don't
make a memorandum of it."*

LEWIS CARROLL
Through the Looking Glass and
What Alice Saw There

The sons of the Prophet are brave men and bold
And quite unaccustomed to fear,
But the bravest by far in the ranks of the Shah
Was named Abdul Abul-Bul Amir.

This son of the desert, in battle aroused,
Could spit twenty men on his spear.
A terrible creature when sober or soused
Was Abdul Abul-Bul Amir.

Now the heroes were plenty and well known to fame
In the troops that were led by the Czar,
And the bravest of these was a man by the name
Of Ivan Skavinsky Skavar.

He could imitate Irving, play poker and pool,
And strum on the Spanish guitar.
In fact, quite the cream of the Muscovite team
Was Ivan Skavinsky Skavar.

The ladies all loved him, his rivals were few.
He could drink them all under the bar.
Half gallon or tank, there was no one so rank
As Ivan Skavinsky Skavar.

One day this bold Russian had shouldered his gun
And donned his most truculent sneer.
Downtown he did go, where he trod on the toe
Of Abdul Abul-Bul Amir.

"Young man," quoth Abdul, "has life grown so dull
That you're anxious to end your career?
Vile infidel, know, you have trod on the toe
Of Abdul Abul-Bul Amir!"

Said Ivan, "My friend, your remarks in the end
Will avail you but little, I fear,
For you ne'er will survive to repeat them alive,
Mr. Abdul Abul-Bul Amir!"

"Now take your last look at sunshine and brook
And send your regrets to the Czar—
For by this I imply you are going to die,
Count Ivan Skavinsky Skavar!"

Then the bold Mameluke drew his trusty skibouk
With a great cry of "Allah Akbar!"
And with murderous intent he ferociously went
For Ivan Skavinsky Skavar.

They fought all that night, 'neath the pale yellow moon.
The din—it was heard from afar,
And huge multitudes came, so great was the fame
Of Abdul and Ivan Skavar.

As Abdul's long knife was extracting the life—
In fact, he had shouted "Huzzah!"—
He felt himself struck by that wily Kalmuck,
Count Ivan Skavinsky Skavar.

The Sultan drove by in his red-breasted fly,
Expecting his victor to cheer,
But he only drew nigh to hear the last sigh
Of Abdul Abul-Bul Amir.

Czar Petrovich, too, in his spectacles blue,
Rode up in his new-crested car.
He arrived just in time to exchange a last line
With Ivan Skavinsky Skavar.

There's a tomb rises up where the blue Danube rolls,
And engraved there in characters clear
Is, "Stranger, when passing, oh pray for the soul
Of Abdul Abul-Bul Amir."

A Muscovite maiden her love vigil keeps
'Neath the light of the pale polar star,
And the name that she murmurs so oft as she weeps
Is Ivan Skavinsky Skavar.

ABDUL Abul-Bul Amir

The sons of the proph~et are brave men and bold And quite un~ac cus~tomed to fear ~ but the

DEBORAH RAY

studied at the Philadelphia College of
Art, the Pennsylvania Academy of the Fine
Arts, the Albert Barnes Foundation and
the University of Pennsylvania, as well
as in France and Italy, and has exhibited
her work in many art shows. In 1967 she
received the Mabel Rush Homer Award of
Woodmere Art Gallery and a Louis Comfort
Tiffany Foundation grant. She lives with
her sculptor husband and two small
daughters in the Germantown area
of Philadelphia.